Fairies FOREVER

World of Fairies

Phidal

What Are Fairies?

Fairies are tiny magical creatures who live deep in the forest, far away from the human world. Use your stickers to find out what they are known for.

Fairies can fly.

Fairies have wands.

Fairies are tiny.

Fairies can dance.

Home Sweet Home

While fairy homes may look small to you, they are just the right size for fairies. Can you find out where they live with the help of your stickers?

In mushrooms

In tree trunks

In hollow hills

In flowers

Time for Dinner!

Little fairies have big appetites. After all, they need a lot of energy to fly all day long. Discover what they like to eat and drink with your stickers.

Honey

Cake

Fruit

T

Full Moon Festival

Fairies welcome every full moon with an enthusiastic celebration filled with song and dance. Put on a party with your stickers.

Favorite Hobbies

Every fairy has a favorite hobby. With your stickers, can you find the tools each fairy needs to perform her special task?

Baking a fairy cake

Playing fairy music

Doing fairy magic

Growing a fairy garden

Magical Jobs

Grown-up fairies can choose from plenty of enchanting jobs. Can you pair up each fairy with her special talent?

Tooth fairy

Song fairy

Love fairy

Wind fairy

15

Dazzling Dresses

Fairy fashions are often inspired by nature, like flowers and leaves. Find out what their dresses are made of with your stickers.

Part
2

Talented Teachers

Young fairies study all types of exciting subjects in fairy school. Can you pair up each talented fairy teacher with the subject that she teaches?

Gardening Teacher

Swimming Teacher

Spell-Casting Teacher

Flying Teacher

Please Be Prepared!

Oops! These little fairies have forgotten some of their dance clothes! Help them whirl and twirl in style by placing your stickers over the right shadows.

Wand Magic

In spell-casting class, these fairies are learning the basics of wand magic. Use your stickers to perform these enchanting tasks.

on and off

open and closed

full and empty

young and old

big and small

Let's Make Music!

The fairies assemble for music class in the heart of the magical forest. Help them play a pretty tune with your stickers.

Classroom Counting

A fairy classroom is filled with many supplies. You may even find some of these in your own school! Count and match each object with a number sticker.

1 hat

2 bees

3 inkwells

4 desks

5 feathers

10 dragonflies

9 apples

6 books

7 wands

8 butterflies

Nature Studies

It is important for young fairies to study nature. Learn about the fairies' surroundings by placing each sticker in the right nature category.

Elements

Water Creatures

Plants

Insects

What's Missing?

It's graduation day for these happy fairies. Can you make the scene below look like the one above with your stickers?

Part 3

Favorite Seasons

Just like you, fairies have their favorite time of year. Using your stickers, can you match each fairy with the season that she likes best?

Winter Fun!

Fairies love to play in the fluffy snow in wintertime. Help these fairies enjoy the cold weather by placing your stickers in the correct scene.

Catching snowflakes

Skiing

Skating

Building snowfairies

Building forts

Sledding

Making snow angels

Snowshoeing

5

Bring on Spring!

Springtime is a very busy season for the fairies. Bring the landscape to life with your stickers by helping them grow bright blooms and sprouts.

Cloud Shapes

On a hot summer day, the fairies have magically transformed the clouds into familiar shapes. Can you identify them with the help of your stickers?

Welcome, Fall!

The fairies have plenty to do before wintertime. Can you help them transform the fall forest with your stickers?

Grow pumpkins

Gather nuts

Harvest wheat

Set the sun earlier

Turn the leaves red

Scatter the leaves

Plant bulbs

Lead the birds south

Rainbow Painters

After a rainfall, the fairies spread a cheerful rainbow across the sky. Can you match each fairy with the band of color that she is painting?

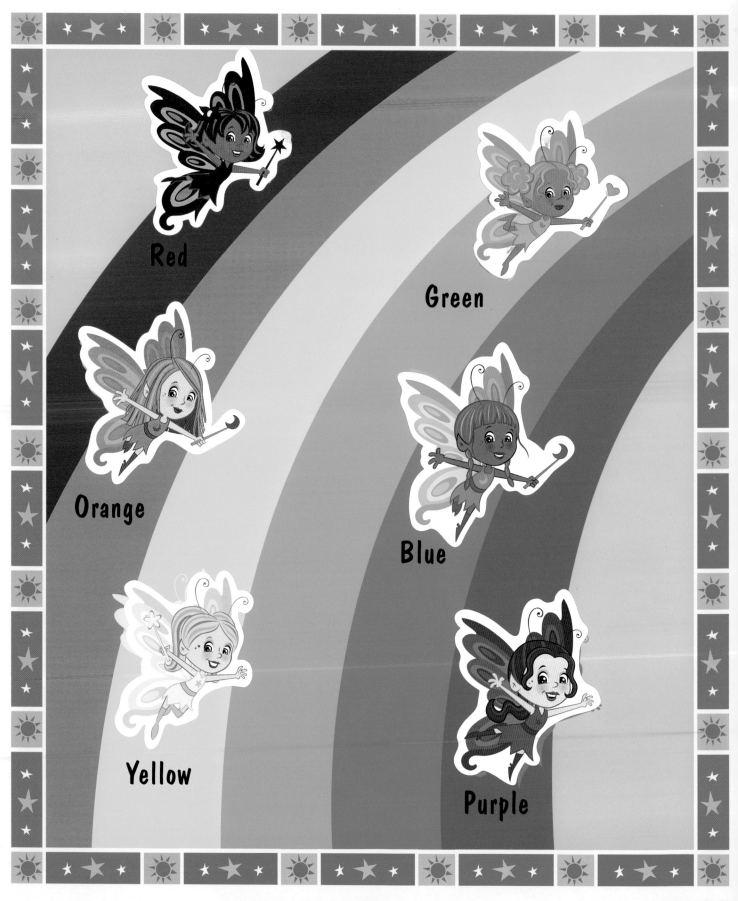

Red

Green

Orange

Blue

Yellow

Purple

Part
4

Cheerful Creatures

Fairies share the forest with many friendly animals, big and small. Can you place each sticker above the correct animal name?

Swan

Dragonfly

Squirrel

Butterfly

Rabbit

Ladybug

Frog

Bird

Butterfly Patterns

Butterflies come in all shapes and colors. Can you place each butterfly in the box that matches its wing pattern?

Strange Species

Be prepared to see some wacky animals in the magical fairy forest! Use your stickers to discover each silly animal combination.

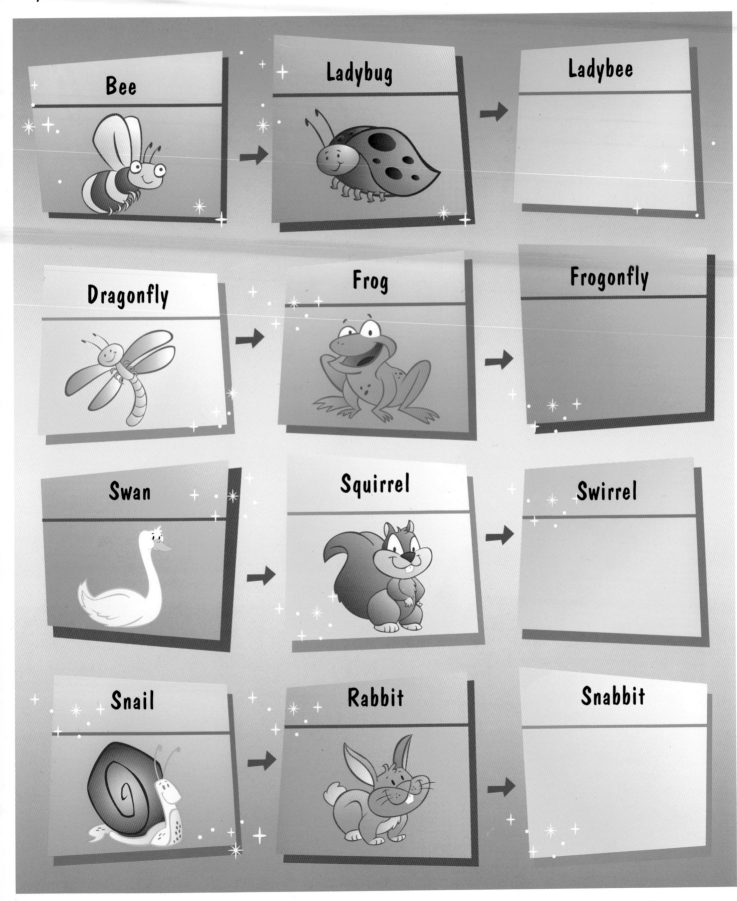

Race Day

The fairies and their animal friends sprint through the forest on a sunny afternoon. Who will be the winner? Bring this race to life with your stickers.

Guess Who?

All animals have special features that make them unique. Can you answer these questions with your stickers?

Who chirps?

Who swims?

Who buzzes?

Who hops?

Happy Helpers

Fairies and their animal friends work very well together. Using your stickers, can you place them in the right scenes?

Fireflies light up the path at night.

Swans offer a soft place to rest.

Dragonflies help collect fairy dust.

Turtles make great instruments.

Birds can sing sweet music.

Shrews can dig holes in the garden.

Where Do They Roam?

Animals live in every corner of the magical fairy forest, from the ground to the water to the sky. Place the animals in their habitat with your stickers.

Sky

Water

Ground